MOTHERS AND BABIES OF THE
MOUNTAINS

by
Roberto Piumini
Translated from the Italian and edited by
Maureen Spurgeon
Illustrations by
Lorella Rizzatti

The first look outside

The marmot's lair is quite a big place! What with metres and metres of tunnels, little rooms for going to the toilet, wide bends, narrow bends, some rising up, others sloping down. . . Little Marmot was two years old, but he still hadn't managed to explore it all!

It was a great game, trying to find his way around. Better still, if he could find the way out. . .

On and on he went, turning this way and that, sniffing *every* so often and trying *every* direction – until, at last, the smell of fresh air and the scent of flowers told him that he must be at the opening!

Very carefully he put his nose outside and sniffed all around. Then came his face, his little ears and the rest of his head, followed by his clear brown front paws.

The opening to the lair was above ground level, at the top of a great pile of earth and stones – like a little mountain with cavities.

But the mountains which Little Marmot could *see* were much, much higher. He sat himself down on his hind legs and looked round at the peaks and the clusters of rock, the snow and the ice glinting in the light, with the valley pastures all around and the dark green expanse of the woods far below. The air was so sweet and fresh, with a breeze rippling through the little pink and blue flowers nestling among the yellow grass of the alpine meadow.

"What are you doing up there?" asked a voice behind him.

Little Marmot smelt a familiar, friendly sort of smell. It was another marmot, very nearly adult, and bigger than him! As it happened, he had seen this marmot once before in the lair, and wanted to make friends.

"Er, just looking. . ." the Little Marmot replied.

"And what tastes there are to look at!" joked the other. "Do you fancy looking at something sweet, like those flowers? Or salty, like this blade of grass?"

The little marmot eyed his companion suspiciously. How could anyone look at tastes? Tastes. . . like flowers, cool, salty grass. . . Ooh, he felt hungry!

And with a flip of his tail, Little Marmot jumped down from the heap of grass and stones at the entrance to the lair.

Then he nosed around among the grass. What a lovely smell! The wind began blowing harder, but the little marmot's coat was so thick, he barely felt it. "Another few days," said his new marmot friend, "and you will leave the lair for good. Then you will have to start making one of your own!"

But Little Marmot was not listening. With his face in the soft earth, he was blissfully eating a nice, juicy root!

The marmot

Marmots are known for their squeaky little voices and the way they behave together. Two marmots will often sit facing each other, seeming to talk noisily, just as if they were having a friendly chatter!

Baby marmots like nothing more than a friendly fight! At the top of the lair, they will push and bump into each other, with both of them finally rolling over together, down to the ground!

The marmot's soft fur protects it from the cold – but this is also the reason why it is hunted by man, with the risk of making this animal extinct.

A walk through the snow

The Saint Bernard puppy was following his mother up and up through the fresh falls of snow. Head down, he sniffed around to the left, then to the right.

"Mother," said the little dog at last. "Can you smell something? I'm sure I can. . ."

"Wait. . ." Mother Saint Bernard thrust her nose towards the snow, scratching a little with her paw.

"No," she said after a while. "No, nothing here!"

They had been on their way back to the rescue shelter for twenty minutes, just after the latest snowfall which had covered the mountain. All was silence, except for the swoop of a raven's wing, black against the white sky.

"Are we going to do a rescue, mother?" the puppy asked her, his tongue hanging out. "Shall we find a poor, lost mountain climber? Or save somebody buried by an avalanche of snow?"

The little puppy knew that many people had been saved by Saint Bernard dogs in the past. Many evenings had been spent by the fireside in the shelter listening as the oldest dog told him about all his adventures.

"But the most famous of us all," he would say, "was big Barry! He lived a century and a half ago, the bravest dog along the whole Saint Bernard Pass, in the whole of the Alps! And do you know how many lives Barry saved? Over fifty, that's how many!"

From then on, the Saint Bernard puppy was determined to make his mark as a rescuer, just like the great Barry! And so, he followed in his mother's huge footprints, watching everything she did.

"Mother," he barked excitedly, "Mother, I'm sure I can smell something! Is it a rescue, do you think?"

The mother dog stopped and sniffed hard.

"There must be something here," she decided after a pause. "I smell it, too!"

And she began digging hard with her front paws, making little heaps of snow all around as she dug.

The Saint Bernard puppy knew then that this was not the time for asking any more questions! Barry would never have chatted away during a rescue – he would have started digging with all his might!

"Here we are!" barked the Mother Saint Bernard. And she pulled out of the snow – a beautiful, white bone and gave it a shake. Now, the puppy's tongue drooped in disappointment.

But, then, the thought of a lovely bone to gnaw made him cheer up! He slid down into the snow, its white flakes powdering his thick coat.

The Saint Bernard dog

If it is true that a dog is man's best friend, then the Saint Bernard dog must take pride of place. Brave and loving, it can face all dangers, thanks to its keen sense of smell and strength in pulling to safety people buried under avalanches of snow.

Saint Bernard puppies are very playful and lively little dogs. Not even the cruel weathers of the mountains can subdue or dampen down their energy!

At birth, a Saint Bernard puppy already weighs one kilo (2.20lbs) – and before it is two years old it will reach a weight of 100 kilos (250lbs).

My gift to the world

The female chamois climbed slowly up the steep, rocky slope, stopping every so often and lifting her head. She was not quite so agile as she usually was – but she was still a chamois, and few other animals were able to get up so high.

She made her way along a rocky ledge, then began threading her way through a gap between the rocks with

a series of short jumps, getting higher and higher. Down below, she might well be disturbed by the herd and the birds fluttering around. And she wanted to find the quietest, most peaceful place, before she gave the most wonderful gift to the world.

All at once, a black shadow caught her eye, and she lifted her head. High up, an eagle circled slowly around, protecting its nest.

No. . . she was not yet at the right place. . . .

She turned away in the other direction. For a whole hour she went on, climbing up rocky slopes, and down little valleys, along grassy pathways and steep ravines, getting slower and slower, until she had to stop and have a drink of water from a mountain stream. And as she drank, she looked all around, her ears twitching back and forth.

Slowly, she set off again. Soon, she could see hills and valleys, with creamy white clouds above. Not a soul was in sight as she made her way behind a rock and climbed up. Here, surely, was the quietest place of the whole mountain.

She nibbled at the grass between some stones and licked a salty rock. But she was not really hungry.

Bending her legs, she crouched down on the ground. But she kept her head straight up, looking ahead with her big, black eyes, listening with long, pointed ears. The two curved little horns on her head made a "V" shape against the blue of the sky.

Then, slowly, slowly, she began to shudder as strong spasms ran through her brown body. And with each sharp push, her huge eyes closed, as if in thought and concentration.

But, in the end — and after quite a long time — she became a mother! She gave birth to a baby chamois, damp and warm and trembling a little, but opening his mouth and nuzzling towards her, in search of her milk.

And Mother Chamois bent her head, feeling so happy as she watched him.

The chamois

The chamois is amongst the most agile animals which we know. It can achieve and keep a perfect balance on a rock which may be only as large as a human hand.

In the mating season, the male chamois become very warlike. One male will point his horns at his rivals and go straight into the attack. And yet, the battle of head against head never seems to cause any harm!

The chamois is quite a friendly, sociable sort of animal, usually living in groups of ten or twenty. It is only when their babies are due that the females go away to give birth in absolute solitude.

An actress for a mother

The seven brown eggs, spotted with yellow, were nearly all hatched. Nearly, but not quite. There was still one to go. The white partridge's six little chicks toddled all around their mother – and she had one eye on them, and the other on the last egg to be hatched. But when this began moving around, she knew that her seventh chick was about to be born.

Suddenly, the mother partridge heard a light, rustling sort of sound. Keeping perfectly still, she quickly covered the chicks with her wing, keeping them in the dark to calm them. She stretched her long, feathered neck, looking out towards the meadow.

A fox, not too big but already very cunning, was slowly zig-zagging his way across the grass, sniffing and keeping his tail well down. He had picked up the partridge's scent, but had not yet seen where she was.

Mother Partridge was not waiting for the fox to get any nearer! She flew out of the nest (which was nothing more than a hole in the grass), and went off, suddenly stopping a short distance away. She looked rather strange, with her right wing stretched out and drooping towards the earth as if it were broken, flapping her other wing very noisily.

The fox, now a short distance below, lifted his head, then kept quite still. Watching this big bird, his tail swished to and fro in mounting satisfaction. Then slowly, he took one step towards her . . . .

The partridge, as if suddenly regaining her strength, at once took off in jagged, desperate flight using only one wing! Then she seemed to fall about ten metres, (30ft) hurtling down towards a rock! Mouth hanging open expectantly, the fox at once trotted towards her. . . .

When he was no more than two metres (6ft) away, he stopped, ready to leap on her. But just then, Mother Partridge made another of her bumpy flights, almost touching the ground as she cleared the rock, dragging her right wing and making for the woods.

The fox chased her as far as he could. But unluckily for him, the partridge had already reached the edge of the trees, where it was more shady. Very downcast, the fox could only sneeze with the dust which the partridge's injured wing had blown around!

And he had been looking foward to a delicious meal!

Then he saw a flash of white in the wood – a flash of white which rose strongly in flight then vanished between the branches. And whilst Mother Partridge was flying to her nest, away from danger and with the seventh egg well and truly hatched – the fox was lost in the wood, far from home and very, very hungry!

The white partridge

Nature has given the white partridge a very extensive wardrobe! During the winter, its feathers are white, in summer they turn to grey streaked with yellow, in spring they are chestnut brown, then in autumn they are dark grey!

When the white partridge decides to have a family, it will find a hen and swoop around in flight in order to show off its feathers. Then, it will invite the hen to fly with him, before they mate together high up in the sky.

Watch out for that bear!

"We must go up into the tree, little one!" called Mother Lynx, her furry head appearing between the branches.

"Why Mother?" the lynx cub asked. "It's hard work getting right up there!"

The little lynx already weighed ten kilos (22lbs), and at the points of his ears he had beautifully straight tufts of fur.

He could jump easily across a stream and creep up on a rabbit in absolute silence. His mother did the hunting, but he was happy enough watching her and eating everything she caught! He just did not feel like going up a tree. . . .

"It's nice here," he protested, swishing his stump of a tail.

With hardly a sound, Mother Lynx jumped down from the branch, landing on her four feet right in front of her cub.

"Now listen to me," she said, crouching down in the grass. The tips of her ears stood up like two tall, dark rods.

"We are not animals of speed, little one," Mother Lynx went on. "Not fast like the cheetah, but with more endurance. Not so much endurance as the wolf, but faster. But neither endurance nor speed is our main weapon, our main defence."

Little Lynx was listening hard now, nestling close to his mother, and licking his glossy, dark summer coat – not quite so thick as the one for winter.

"We know how to jump," Mother Lynx continued calmly, "but not like the puma. And we are not big enough to knock a deer to the ground, either."

She paused, looking at her cub.

The forest wind blew the thick side-whiskers of the mother lynx, so that they stood out like a little forest of light around her muzzle.

"And so, little one, we must go up into the trees. That way, we can jump down from a height on our prey, making the most of a sudden and powerful attack! No other beast does this, did you know that?"

The little lynx seemed far from convinced. He yawned, and began washing himself lazily.

At that moment, Mother Lynx cried, "Look out! A bear!" And in a flash, she was on her feet, jumping halfway up the trunk and safely on to a branch!

The lynx cub was too scared to do anything, except follow his mother, landing on the branch with her!

"We've escaped!" he cried. "Where is the bear?"

"He was over there!" said his mother. "But now, he has gone – just like your laziness!"

So the lynx cub had learned two things that day. First, that it was easy to jump up in a tree. And second, there are many ways of getting what you want!

The lynx

The forest is the ideal environment for the life which a lynx leads. Squatting on the branch of a tree, this cat will wait for exactly the right moment to jump down on its prey.

The lynx will not put up with having an empty stomach in winter-time! This is when it will come down from the trees and move swiftly across the snow, thanks to the thick fur covering the under-sides of its paws.

Little Guanaco on the defence

"Hey, Guanaco! Little Guanaco!" cried the shepherd in the Andes Mountains, holding out a handful of grass.

He was a short, dark-skinned man, wearing a multi-coloured woollen cape, with a little woollen cap on his head.

"Hey, Little Guanaco!" he cried again. "Come here!"

He began taking tiny, little steps, trying to get nearer. The little guanaco had got lost from the rest of the herd, trying to reach the meadow after a thunderstorm. The other guanacos, watched by the male leader of the herd, were on a grassy slope, a little further up the mountain.

"Come along, beautiful!" the shepherd called. "Let me take you to my pen down in the village! You'll be fine there, along with your cousins, the llamas! I'll give you grass, and the llamas will tell you, you won't ever carry me on your back! There are only two llamas in my pen, you know that, Little Guanaco?"

The little guanaco wanted to take the fresh grass which the man held out, but he was afraid. He took two steps back, lifting each of his legs in turn. He felt as if he wanted to spit. . . .

"Come on, come on, don't be scared! It's lovely in the village! Look, I'll put you near my two alpaca goats. They're your cousins, too! They have a beautiful coat, warm and long, and when the wind blows from the Andes Mountains, you will be able to lie down with them and keep warm! Come along!"

And the shepherd, with more tiny, little steps, came up the grassy slope towards the guanaco.

But the little guanaco spat out, straight and strong, hitting the man right in the face! Then as he stopped in surprise, the little animal turned and ran for its life, back to where he thought he had last seen the herd. In a few minutes he saw it again, scattered underneath a line of rocks.

The guanacos were nibbling at the short grass, but not all at the same time. Whilst some of the herd lowered their heads to graze, others kept watch all around, heads raised up. Then, those keeping watch began to graze, leaving the others to lift their heads to keep a look-out.

And at the edge of the herd, the little guanaco saw his mother. She was looking out for him, trotting anxiously back and forth. He ran to her so happily, lifting up clods of earth with his little hooves.

The guanaco

Unfortunately the gentle guanaco can be quite a fighter. When two animals of the same herd clash, they both try to bite into the enemy's legs, or twist the neck to make a killing.

The home of the guanaco is a vast area spreading over the Terra del Fuoco (meaning Land of Fire) in Peru, South America. The guanaco originally descended from two tame animals – the llama and the alpaca goat.

The guanaco is not very gallant towards the female during the mating season. Whether she accepts or ignores his advances, the male will spit furiously at her!

A lesson in hunting

"Now, pay attention!" said Mother Puma. "Listen to me, and watch all that I do!"

The mother and baby puma were at a forest clearing where the grass was fairly low, and with a few moss-covered rocks, here and there. The ground was flat, sloping down gently towards the stream which flowed a short distance away.

"Now," said Mother Puma, "when we approach our prey, we must keep back a little, and stay at a slightly higher level. It's easier then to jump and attack. . . ."

The little puma, sitting there like a cat, listened carefully to his mother's instructions. The blotches on his coat with which he was born could still be seen, but these were fast disappearing. A few months more, and he would have a new coat, the same brown colour all over, just like the adult puma. The only difference would be the black tip of the tail – like that which Mother Puma was now swishing low over the grass.

"Stop looking at my tail, little one," she scolded, "and pay attention! Now, I shall show you how to make the jump. The right position is most important!"

Slowly, Mother Puma arched her back, stretching out her paws from under her shoulders and placing her feet firmly on the ground. Keeping her hind legs just a little higher than her front paws, every muscle in the mother puma's body was tensed up, ready to spring.

Then she leapt so fast that the baby puma was left looking at the spot where she had taken off! And about ten metres ahead, the Mother Puma turned and came back towards him.

"You see?" she called. "With two or three jumps like that, you can capture a deer or a hare before they even notice us, let alone have chance to escape! Now you try, little one!"

Obediently, the little puma crouched down on the grass, bringing his legs together. Then, arching his back, and with his tail in a curve, he tried to get himself in exactly the same position as his mother.

"How many jumps did you say it takes to capture our prey?" he asked, staring hard at an imaginary young deer.

"Three, or four at the most," Mother Puma answered. "Usually three jumps will cover a good stretch of ground quite fast enough, and here. . ."

She did not manage to finish. With a funny little skid, the baby puma was away! His first jump was not all that big. But with the second, he really stretched himself – and the third would have been wonderful if he had managed a proper landing. But, the baby puma had not calculated the distance. He finished up in the stream, with a loud splash!

"You can stay on the bank if you want to fish for frogs!" said Mother Puma, shaking a spray of water from her whiskers!

The puma

The puma is certainly the member of the cat family who would earn a medal for the champion long jump! After crouching down on its legs, it can make leaps of up to eighteen metres! (58.5 feet).

The young of the puma are lively, graceful little animals, who are never still. Like kittens at home, they are always running, jumping or romping about.

The puma has been hunted for many years, with men wanting to wipe them out because they are a threat to livestock. But slowly, attitudes are changing, and there now seems to be more hope for the puma.

A high-rise baby

It was the first storm of the year along the mountainous coast of Canada. The wind whistled through the bare trees and the rocks, scattering the snow in all directions and creating a strange sort of white-tinged darkness.

In a little cave, Mother Mountain Goat and her kid waited patiently. And as the wind blew in through the

opening, it ruffled the white fur around their necks, stroking its icy fingers along their woolly backs. But the kid and its mother were not cold.

"Must we stay here very long, mother?" asked the little goat. This was the first winter the kid had known. It had been born in summertime, when the mountainside was covered in tender grass to eat.

"We can go outside once the storm is over," Mother Goat answered. "If we leave before that, we shall not be able to see the way. In a storm, we cannot hear sounds or smell scents, either, which means we could easily be taken by a bear or a puma."

"But there's nothing to eat here!" said the little goat. "What food will there be, outside?"

"If we cannot find any grass underneath the snow," said the mother goat, "then we shall eat the soft moss. And there will be some wild plants to taste!"

By this time, the wind was not whistling quite so loud and the snow was not falling quite so thick. Soon, the storm had died down, as if it had never been, the mountains all around white and silent. Further down, the forest looked like an enormous herd of goats, completely still.

The mother goat got up, and, lowering her head so as not to bump her horns, edged her way through the opening and out on to a narrow, rocky ledge.

The baby goat followed her – and although he only had tiny, little horns, he solemnly lowered his head, too, just as Mother Mountain Goat had done. Trusting his mother as he did, he always did exactly the same as her.

Slowly, the two mountain goats began making their way down the steep mountainside. Like his mother, the kid chose exactly the right places to put his hooves, which could spread out slightly and close around stones and rocks to get a firm grip.

They found themselves on an overhanging spur of rock. Should they turn away and go higher, or jump down? A little way below, the ground sloped gently down towards snow-covered trees and some bushes.

"Remember how to jump?" asked the Mother Goat.

The kid made a sign to say yes, he did. He pointed his head downwards and jumped from the rock, lifting his head just before landing safe and sound on all four feet.

He could already smell the scent of leaves beneath the snow.

The mountain goat

If the mountain goat is a perfect balancing artiste when it comes to jumping on rocks, her kid soon shows that he is equal to the situation! He can stand on his feet only ten minutes after being born, and at three days old, he is already able to start climbing!

There are two main enemies of the mountain goat – the bear, and, of course, man. The first hunts the mountain goat for food, the second for its beautiful, white, soft goatskin.

Living so high up, the mountain goat enjoys the most wonderful views. No wonder it will often sit and just look around at the beautiful surroundings.

Mother, where are you?

The snow-storm had lasted the whole day long, and still it showed no signs of easing off. No human being was in sight, and the few animals which lived three thousand metres (9,750 feet) above sea level in the Tibetan mountains were either sheltering in caves or inside their lairs, away from the icy wind and the blinding whiteness. All they were aware of was the wail of the storm as more

snow fell upon snow, thickly and without making a sound.

But – something was moving. At first, it seemed like chunks of the mountain itself, huge, heavy rocks, but with horns. . . . Solid, plastered with snow, and with heads lowered, the yak moved slowly along the track, now scarcely visible on the mountainside.

"Mother, where are you?" called a baby yak, walking behind an enormous male beast about a ton in weight.

"Mother, are you there?" called the baby yak again, thrusting his head against the cruel wind.

He could not see too well, because of the snow whirling around and also the fur which fell down over his forehead and his eyes.

"I am here, little one," came Mother Yak's voice from behind. "What is the matter?"

"I could not see you!" came the reply.

"And where did you think I had gone?" she asked, nuzzling his tail with her warm nose. "We yaks, you know, are very slow, and so we do not move fast at all. But, we keep moving!"

"But, why are we so slow?" asked the little yak. He wanted to carry on hearing his mother's voice!

"Partly because we know there are hidden dangers on the mountain," Mother Yak told him. "But, like us, the mountain is big and powerful — and very, very still. That teaches us yaks something!"

"And so, mother?" persisted the baby yak.

"And so, we are very slow, because that is how we conserve our energy. Why waste it, living here where nothing much happens?" And Mother Yak gave her little one a gentle push with her nose to get him moving again.

At the head of the herd, the big male yak was leading the way between some overhanging rocks, behind which the wind blew less strongly, and the snow fell more slowly. Here, the yak could stop and spend the night, huddled close together.

The yak

The yak is the largest of the ox family to be found in the whole of Asia. With an average weight of one ton, it has horns almost one metre (39 inches) in length, and is over two metres (6.5 feet) high!

The yak can survive in extremely harsh conditions. The icy storms which blow across the mountains of the Himalayas do not bother this beast, protected as it is by a long, thick coat of fur.

In some countries of Central Asia, the yak is a valuable vehicle for journeys in the mountains. With each slow and plodding step, it can carry on its back loads of over 150 kilos! (375lbs).

How pandas fight!

Three thousand metres (9,750 feet) high up in the mighty mountains of the Himalayas, there is also a dense, green forest, home of birds, mammals, insects and reptiles, with running streams and waterfalls.

Here, the Minor Panda's baby was now two and a half months old. He weighed 1,500 grammes, (3lbs), including his thick bushy tail.

The baby panda's fur was a lovely russet red on top, with a glossy black underneath. He lived with another baby panda and Mother and Father Panda among the tall trees of the forest, and had already learned to move around easily.

"Let's have a game!" suggested his sister. She was a lively little panda, but rather crafty, as well.

"All right!" said the panda cub, and rose up on his hind legs, moving his front paws about in the air in fast, little circles!

"This is how we pandas fight!" he told her. Only the day before, during one of the family's rare walks on the ground in search of bamboo shoots, the panda cub had watched an old male panda having to face up to a fierce-looking bear. And, with paws raised, this panda had made the bear retreat back from their part of the forest.

Although the old panda was the smaller of the two, his actions had frightened the bear so much, that he had turned and run away on all fours towards the lower regions of the forest!

"See if you can reach the end of the branch, brave panda!" cried his sister, backing away from him.

The panda cub did not hesitate. He followed her quite confidently. With his sharp claws and the fur on his soles so that he did not slip, going to the end of the branch was no problem at all!

Towards the end, the branch narrowed. Here, the panda's sister held on tight as she called out to him, "Now, how did you say pandas fight?"

Without thinking, the panda cub rose up on his hind legs, pretending to fight two angry bears at once. But, at that very moment, his sister shook the branch hard, making it bounce. The panda cub struggled to try and keep hold of the branch – but he lost his balance and fell down below, his bushy tail fluttering behind him!

"Now I've seen how pandas fall!" his sister cried out cheekily.

And down below, the panda cub puffed and fumed, before he began climbing up again. Why, he thought, did he have to be caught out by that pest of a little sister?

The minor panda

Danger lying in wait? The minor panda just gives a few great big jumps to safety in the trees. Too bad that the enemy down below is disappointed!

The minor panda is a very clean animal. When it is time for washing and grooming, he will lick the insides of his paws very carefully, and use these to wash his face and ears!

Both likeable and harmless, the minor panda is under the threat of extinction, being hunted by man for its soft, red fur.

Index